Real Women

Exploring together what a
Christian woman thinks and does

14 sessions in Colossians

Sarah Bradley

For Georgia

and with thanks to Ruth, Megan, Esme and all the others who helped trial this book

One2One Real Women

© The Good Book Company 2013

The Good Book Company
Blenheim House, 1 Blenheim Road
Epsom, Surrey KT19 9AP
Tel (UK): 0333 124 0880
Tel (US): 866 244 2165
Tel (int): +(44) 208 942 0880
email: info@thegoodbook.co.uk

Websites:
UK & Europe: www.thegoodbook.co.uk
North America: www.thegoodbook.com
Australia: www.thegoodbook.com.au
New Zealand: www.thegoodbook.co.nz

ISBN: 9781909559059

Printed in China

A real woman

Long hair, short hair, make up, bare face, skirt or trousers...

Married, single, kids, no kids, stay-at-home mum or high-flying business woman...

What makes a real woman?

Many people would have us believe that the perfect figure, a gorgeous man and a go-getter attitude that says: "I'm here, I'm confident and I can do anything", is what makes a real woman. Is that really true?

There's so much more, and there's so much that's better.

A real woman is one who knows who she is in Jesus. She's someone who looks in the mirror and even on a low day or a bad-hair day or a spotty day, says, sometimes through tears, sometimes through smiles: "I'm a forgiven child of God and I'm going to live for him".

Over the next few weeks, this booklet will take you through the Bible book of Colossians, and help you to see how awesome Jesus is, how important it is to be rooted in him and how that affects the way we live and the relationships we have with the people around us.

Whatever type of women you are now, or grow to be in the future, if you get this right and your roots are in the right place, you'll be living as the person you were created to be.

contents

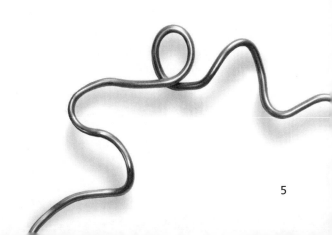

Rooted in Christ Jesus

Paul followed Jesus. He shared the good news of Jesus in many different places, and it wasn't always easy. He was imprisoned, beaten, and shipwrecked, and yet he kept on going.

He believed that passing on the truth about Jesus had to happen no matter what!

Total turnaround

But Paul wasn't always like that. At one time he hated Jesus and all his followers. He didn't just talk about them behind their backs, he wanted to imprison and execute them.

One day, while Paul was on a journey to get rid of some Christians, Jesus appeared to him, and it transformed his life (you can read about it in Acts 9 v 1-19).

Instead of wanting people to hate Jesus, now Paul wanted them to love and follow Jesus. Some people hated his message, some tried to get rid of him—but some became Christians, churches were started and the good news spread.

Paul and the Colossians

Colossae was a little town in western Turkey. The church had been started by Epaphras, who was a faithful worker with Paul (Colossians 1 v 7). Paul couldn't visit the Colossian church because he was in prison, so he wrote to them to encourage them.

How brilliant it must have been for the Colossian Christians to know that even though Paul couldn't be with them, he was thinking of them and praying for them.

They were loving Jesus and they were growing—but there was a danger that some extra things were creeping in, things that suggested they needed *more* than just Jesus to really follow him.

Paul wants to make it clear that Jesus is enough. Paul wants to remind them how amazing Jesus is, so they know that loving and serving him is all they need.

It's this letter, called Colossians, which you're going to be getting into over the next few weeks.

How this booklet works

In here you'll find 14 sessions, each looking at a bit of Colossians.

Seven sessions (the odd-numbered ones) are JOINT, for you to do with an older Christian woman—just the two of you (or you and a friend and her). The other seven (the even-numbered ones) are SOLO, for you to do on your own in your own time.

So it'll take you seven weeks to do the whole booklet if you meet up weekly, 14 if you meet up every two weeks. When you get together, it'll probably take you 45 minutes to do the session. On your own, the sessions should take around half an hour at the most.

Lots of people find it helpful to write down answers to some, or all, of the questions—it helps you focus on the question, and remember what you found in the Bible. So there are spaces left to scribble something down. But if the thought of having to write stuff down makes you want to close this book, then don't feel you have to!

You may well have been given this booklet by an older woman at your church who leads your youth group, or by your mum; they'll be hoping you can both learn together more about how to be a real woman. Maybe you've found this booklet yourself... if you have, you'll get most out of it if you do it with an older woman who's been a Christian for at least a few years. So try to find one at a church or Christian youth group near you.

It doesn't matter whether you're already a follower of Jesus, or someone who wants to find out about him and what he says. And because this is a booklet for women, it doesn't pull punches or tiptoe round the issues women sometimes find difficult. That's not how real women deal with things.

The Bible quotes in this booklet are from the NIV 2011 (New International Version). If you have, or can get your hands on, that translation, then do— but the sessions will work with Bible versions like the ESV, the NASB, and the NIrV (and probably lots of others!) too.

If you're an older woman wanting to use this booklet with a teenager, you'll find a helpful online guide at www.thegoodbook.co.uk/realwomenguide, which is well worth looking at before you start.

Being thankful Joint

Today's Bible section: Colossians chapter 1, verses 1-8

A GETTING STARTED

1 When was the last time you said thank you?

How many times a day do you think you say thank you?

When was the last time you said thank you to God? What for?

B DEAR CHRISTIANS   Read Colossians 1 v 1-2

Have you noticed that letters in the Bible start a bit like emails? At the top you have who it's from, and then who it's to...

2 How does Paul, the writer of the letter describe himself?

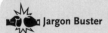 **Jargon Buster**   Apostles = the men God chose to write the New Testament and to set up his church.

3 Why do you think that's important?

4 What does Paul think of the church in Colossae?

It's a positive opening to the letter. Paul describes them as holy people, (set apart by God and for God). These faithful brothers and sisters are receiving a letter of great encouragement from Paul.

Paul hadn't been to Colossae or met these *Gentile* Christians but he had a whole lot to be thankful to God for. The Colossians weren't Jews, so they hadn't been brought up knowing the Old Testament's truths and promises. They were outsiders who had come to know Jesus, which was always God's plan.

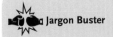 **Jargon Buster** Gentile = not a Jew. There was often rivalry between them. Many Jews didn't think that Gentiles could know God. Paul knew that was wrong.

Paul clearly wasn't a major fan of punctuation, so his sentences can be long and complicated... However, it's well worth diving in and seeing what he has to say.

C | **BEING THANKFUL**   **Read Colossians 1 v 3-4**

---

5 What is Paul always doing?

6 Why?

Paul thanks God for their faith and love. **Read verses 5-7.**

7 Where do faith and love spring from?

 **Jargon Buster** Hope = this isn't an "I hope it rains" or "I hope I pass my exams", ie: a desire with no certainty. In the Bible, hope is a *certain* hope. So, this "hope stored up ... in heaven" is a certain promise that they will be in heaven one day.

Paul thanks God that the Colossians know about the certainty of heaven, and the truth of the gospel.

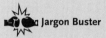 **Jargon Buster** Gospel = "good news". The true message of the gospel is the good news of Jesus' life, death and resurrection, which brings forgiveness for sinners and gives us the certain hope of heaven.

8 Where had the gospel been bearing fruit (verse 6)?

a)

b)

9 How does the gospel bear fruit and grow in the world?

10 When did the gospel begin bearing fruit?

11 How does all this show that the gospel the Colossians know is the gospel that saves (v 6)?

12 What had the Colossians truly understood in verse 6?

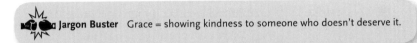

Jargon Buster Grace = showing kindness to someone who doesn't deserve it.

We don't find grace easy. Have you ever been in town, and someone has come up to you and said they have a voucher for a free haircut or makeover? What's your instant response? Mine is: "What's the catch? Nothing's free, so what will I have to do in return?"

We're not used to getting something for nothing. But that's exactly what God's grace is. It's us getting the amazing gift of forgiveness that we don't deserve—and we don't have to do anything, except believe it!

D **STOP AND THINK!**

> Have you truly understood God's grace, or do you feel you have to do
> things to please God and make him love you more?

❸ Can you put into your own words what Paul can give thanks for?

What a list! Paul is writing this letter from prison in Rome, so there aren't any home comforts. But Paul still finds so much to be thankful to God for.

Think back to the question at the beginning of the study: "What was the last thing you thanked God for?" How does your answer compare to Paul's thankfulness for the Colossians?

E **PASSING ON THE GOOD NEWS**   **Read Colossians 1 v 7-8**

❹ Who had taught the Colossians?

Paul had taught Epaphras about Jesus, and then he had passed on the good news to the Colossians.

11

⓯ What did Paul and Epaphras have in common (v 1 and v 7)?

⓰ How did Paul and Epaphras feel about the Colossians?

Epaphras had become a Christian, and passed on the good news to the people. Through his faithful teaching, they had "truly understood God's grace".

PRAYER TIME

◆ Who is/was your "Epaphras"—the one who shared the good news of Jesus with you? (There might be more than one person.)

◆ How did they do it?

Thank God for them, and for his grace in helping you to believe.

◆ Who can you be an "Epaphras" to?

◆ What could you pray for them? How could you pass on the good news?

Pray that you would be faithful in how you share the good news with them.

MEMORY VERSE

"We always THANK GOD, the Father of our Lord Jesus Christ, when we pray for you, because we have heard of your faith in Christ Jesus and of the love you have for all God's people."
Colossians 1 v 3-4

Today's Bible section: Colossians chapter 1, verses 9-14

A GETTING STARTED

❶ What are your prayers like? Who and what do you pray for?

What motivates you to pray?

B PRAYING FOR YOU   Read Colossians 1 v 9-10

This section begins "For this reason..." That means we need to look back at the first eight verses to find the reason. Paul obviously loves to pray. He tells the Colossians that he's always thanking God for their love and faith, and for the true gospel that is bearing fruit.

❷ How important do you think prayer is to Paul?
How do you know (v 9)?

❸ What does Paul pray for the Colossians (v 9)?

4 What is the purpose of the knowledge? There are four things included in verse 10.

Knowing God, and knowing his will, will transform how they live.

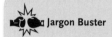 **Jargon Buster** God's will = his great purpose for all his creation, that all his people would hear the good news of Jesus, and be united together under Christ.

5 Why is knowing God's will so important (v 10)?

Read Colossians 1 v 10-12

6 As we are filled with the knowledge of God's will, how will that make a difference in our lives? Complete the table.

Living a life worthy of the Lord and pleasing him means:
v 10b (this means the middle of the verse)
v 10c (this means at the end of the verse)
v 11
v 12

7 Verses 10-12 give us the characteristics of a growing Christian. How would you explain them in your own words?

C GOD'S PLAN   Read Colossians 1 v 12-14

If we know God's ultimate plan for his world—that he wants us to become more like Jesus, and wants people to turn to him in repentance—what will happen? It must make a difference to how we live. It will mean we want the same as God, and as we see him at work, we'll grow in our knowledge of him.

> **STOP!** This is such an exciting prayer to pray, for ourselves and for our Christian brothers and sisters. That's how Paul described Christians in Colossians 1 v 2. We're family! If you ever wonder what to pray for other Christians, why not put their name in this prayer and pray it for them? Pray it for yourself as well.

Paul cannot stop giving thanks (1 v 9). From verses 12-14, he spells out some of the reasons we have to be thankful to God.

8 What had God the Father done for the Colossians, which is true for us too (v 12)?

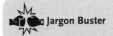 **Jargon Buster**   Kingdom of light = this is another way of describing heaven. A place of goodness and perfection—with God at the centre.

I don't know what inheritance you're expecting one day, maybe from grandparents or parents. Property? Money? Jewels? They're all great, but they're only good or useful for this life. Jesus' inheritance for us is in heaven and, although undeserved, is ours for ever.

15

9 If you are a Christian, what has God the Father done for you (v 13)?

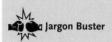

Jargon Buster   Dominion of darkness = bad things often happen at night, such as burglaries and break-ins. People can hide in the darkness. This is another way of describing a place where sin rules; a place where people are slaves to sin. We can be rescued from sin because of Jesus.

10 What do we have in Jesus (v 14)?

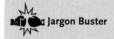

Jargon Buster   Redemption = buying something/someone back at a price. Jesus redeems us. We were slaves to sin, but Jesus' death has paid the price so we can be free.

D   WHAT DO CHRISTIANS BELIEVE?

God made a perfect world, but it's not like that now (turn on the news, watch people or think about your own life.) The reality is that our world is pretty messed up. It can look as if darkness (sin) is winning; that the "dominion of darkness" is more powerful than anything.

Paul reminds us that Christians have been rescued from the dominion of darkness. Jesus has beaten the power of sin, freed people from the slavery of sin and brought forgiveness.

(More in the next study)

PRAYER TIME

It's easy to make prayer self-centred or like a shopping list. I often forget to praise God for what he's done for me, and the amazing promises he's made. This prayer in Colossians encourages us to ask God for good and right things. That doesn't mean that we shouldn't pray about exams, family, illnesses etc... but we should pray about them in light of this prayer.

How could verses 9-14 change the way you pray?

THANK YOU GOD	PLEASE GOD

It's all about Jesus   Joint

Today's Bible section: Colossians chapter 1, verses 15-23

A ...AND THE ANSWER IS?

Quick quiz	
Who had 12 disciples?	
Who fed 5000 people?	
Who calmed a storm?	
Who made the blind see?	
Who was crucified on a cross?	
Who rose 3 days later?	

We're going to see just how amazing Jesus is, and that everything is about him.

❶ If someone asked you who Jesus was, how would you answer?

B IT'S ALL ABOUT JESUS   Read Colossians 1 v 15-20

❷ Who is the Son and what does he show us (v 15)?

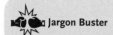 **Jargon Buster**   Firstborn = the firstborn son would traditionally be the heir of his father, and had special rights and privileges.

3 Look at verses 15-20. What repeated words or phrases can you spot?

These verses tell us something crucial about Jesus. As Paul writes to the Colossians, he wants them to know that Jesus is like no other.

4 How was Jesus involved in the creation of the world (v 16)?

5 Why was the world created (v 16b)?

You might think that *God* was always around, but that *Jesus* only showed up when he was born in Bethlehem. These verses tell us that Jesus was at the creation of the world. In Genesis 1:26 God says: "Let US make mankind in our image". Jesus was with God in the beginning.

6 What role does Jesus play in creation now (v 17)?

Not only was Jesus there at the creation of the world, he holds it together and keeps it going. Jesus is crucial to the world existing. The big message from these verses is that Jesus is really important. (What an understatement!)

7 What does verse 18 tell us Jesus is also the head of?

It's easy to see that creation is impressive. I don't have a hard time believing that someone made it, and keeps it going—our world is awesome.

But maybe it's harder to see that when you look at the church. You might love your church or maybe you find it hard. However you feel, Jesus is head of the church too. It's as important as creation. Jesus thinks that church is a big deal!

8 Do you?

9 How is Jesus the firstborn from among the dead (v 18)?

10 Why does that give him supremacy (highest authority) (v 18)?

11 What does verse 19 tell us about Jesus?

12 What else was God pleased to do through Jesus (v 20)?

D RECONCILED

But why was this reconciliation necessary?

Have you ever argued with a friend, and stopped talking to them? Silly question... it's something girls are brilliant at! We hurt each other by what we say and do, and it can be hard to make up. Unkind words and bad treatment get in the way of friendships being as they should.

Our relationship with God is similar but much much worse...

Read Colossians 1 v 21-23

13 How does verse 21 describe our situation with God before becoming a Christian?

Verse 21 makes it clear why reconciliation was necessary. We were living against God in every way. But the great news is that Paul talks about our alienation—our separation from God—in the **past tense**.

14 What has Jesus' death achieved for us if we're Christians (v 22)?

15 What part do we play (v 23)?

Imagine you get into difficulty while swimming in the ocean, and a rescue helicopter is sent to rescue you. One of the rescue team is winched down into the water to attach you to the rope and pull you to safety. What part do you play? Not a lot!

You're in danger. You can't rescue yourself. All you can do is hold on, and keep trusting in your rescuer. If half-way up you decide you don't need them anymore and unclip yourself, you're going straight back into the water. You need to keep holding on and keep trusting! That's the only part you play in your rescue.

That's the great news of the gospel. We need rescuing, but we don't have to do anything; Jesus has done it all. We continue to trust him, continue to believe in the good news just like in the beginning—there is nothing more to do.

PRAYER TIME

Spend some time praising Jesus for being so amazing...

◆ Look again at verses 15-18 and **praise Jesus for who he is**.

◆ Look again at verses 19-23 and **praise Jesus for what he's done**.

MEMORY VERSE

"He has RECONCILED you by Christ's physical body through death to present you holy in his sight."

Colossians 1 v 22

Mystery made clear   **Solo**

Today's Bible section: Colossians chapter 1, verses 24-29

A TOUGH TIMES

1 Have you ever been through a difficult time? How did you feel?

Colossians 4 v 3 tells us that Paul was in prison. It would have been miserable, dirty and damp.

Read Colossians 1 v 24

2 How does Paul feel about his suffering (v 24)?

That seems weird, doesn't it? Rejoicing in suffering? You don't stub your toe and text your friends to tell them the news with great joy! And being in a 1st-century prison was much worse than a stubbed toe!

3 Why can Paul rejoice? Who is he suffering for (v 24)?

Paul's in prison because he won't stop talking about Jesus. And so he rejoices—there's nothing better! He's suffering so that more people can meet Jesus.

B HEALTH WARNING!   Verse 24 is a VERY tricky verse

What it's NOT saying: that there was something missing from Jesus' death and Paul had to suffer to add to it. Colossians 1 v 20-22 shows that Jesus' death achieved **all** that was needed.

What it IS saying: Colossians 1 v 22 says Jesus' death brought reconciliation so that we can be presented holy in God's sight. But we don't see the full evidence of that now. We're not fully reconciled to God, and we're far from perfect. Just as Jesus suffered, his people will suffer in this spoiled world. Paul certainly did! As he suffered, he knew it brought him closer to God, and helped other Christians. Paul knew that one day he would be perfect—as all Christians will.

 Jargon Buster   Reconciliation = bringing together two or more people who have been separated or divided by something.

Read Colossians 1 v 25-27

 Jargon Buster   Commission = the specific role or job Paul had been given.

❹ What must Paul do (v 25)?

❺ What do you think Paul means by "the word of God in its fullness"?

God's word is how we know him. It helps us grow to be more like him. We need to listen regularly to what it says, because it's in God's word that we meet Jesus (v 27).

◖ IT'S A MYSTERY

I love a good mystery story: starting at the beginning, meeting the characters, following the twists and turns to solve the mystery. Inevitably, I guess it wrong, because I don't know what the author was thinking as they wrote. They want to keep you guessing to the end.

Paul mentions a mystery that has been hidden for ages, but now is disclosed to the Lord's people (the saints).

Re-read verses 26-27

6 What mystery has now been revealed? What has God made known?

In the Old Testament, God's people were waiting for the Messiah (Christ)—the chosen one God promised would come into the world to unite God and people. Prophets spoke about him; there were glimpses of what he would be like; but he didn't come. Paul makes it clear that the Messiah has now come... **Jesus** is who they've been waiting for.

7 Which two groups of people has God made the mystery known to (v 26 and 27)?

8 Why is that so amazing? (See Jargon buster: Gentile on page 9.)

In the Old Testament, God's people were the Jews. A few Gentiles were brought in to God's people, but not many. Now Paul says the mystery has been made known among the Gentiles. In other words ANYONE can come to know Jesus!

9 Can we understand the good news of Jesus without God (v 27)? Why/why not?

If I'm reading a mystery book, I can't put it down half way through and say: "The train driver did it—no question!" I don't know. I can't be sure unless I keep reading to the end and the author makes it clear. Unless they reveal it, I'm just guessing. God reveals the mystery of Jesus. He makes it possible for us to know and understand how amazing Jesus is.

🔟 Why do you think Paul describes the mystery as glorious riches? (Look back again at 1 v 22.)

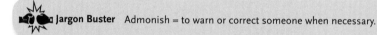

D HOW TO BE MATURE   **Read Colossians 1 v 28-29**

⓫ Why does Paul talk about Jesus (v 28)?

Jargon Buster   Admonish = to warn or correct someone when necessary.

⓬ What do you think it means to be fully mature/perfect in Christ? (Look at 1 v 23 for a further clue.)

⓭ If you become a Christian, will your life stay the same as before? Why/why not?

We're never going to be perfect in this life; our sin will always stop that happening. But because Christians have been *redeemed* by Jesus, we can presented as "fully mature/perfect" before our perfect God.

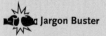 Jargon Buster   Redeemed = buying something/someone back at a price. Jesus redeems us. Everyone is a slave to sin. Jesus' death provides forgiveness for our sin. The price is paid so we can be free.

14 How committed is Paul to telling people about Jesus (v 29)?
Is it easy?

Paul will work hard. He'll suffer. He'll even rejoice in suffering because he is so convinced of the importance of passing on the good news—that Jesus is the revealed mystery everyone has been waiting for. Paul will proclaim it, no matter what, so that people can come to know and love Jesus!

The mystery of Jesus needs to be proclaimed so it's not a mystery to people any more.

STOP AND THINK

Where do you hear the word of God proclaimed?

Is it the word of God in all its fullness? Are there bits of the Bible you've never looked at before?

Do you want to be presented fully mature/perfect in Christ? Why/why not?

PRAYER TIME

◆ Ask God to help you listen to his word.

◆ Ask him to make himself known and make you more like him day by day.

Session 5 | Stick with Jesus

Today's Bible section: Colossians chapter 2, verses 1-7

A GETTING STARTED

1 If you're a Christian—are there things you find hard?
Do you get frustrated sometimes, because you think it should be easier?

If you're not a Christian—are there things in life you find hard?
Do you think life should be easier?

B IT'S A STRUGGLE!   Read Colossians 2 v 1-3

2 What is Paul doing as he writes, and who for (v 1)?

3 Paul has already written about two things he's committed to that aren't always easy. What are they?

a) 1 v 9:

b) 1 v 28:

Paul won't stop because he knows how important they are.

4 What does Paul want for the Colossians (v 2a)?

a)

b)

Paul wants them to have everything that knowing Jesus brings.

5 Why is knowing Jesus so brilliant and worth Paul's contending/
struggle (v 2b-3)?

In the last study we learned that the "mystery" was Christ (Colossians
1 v 26-27). Paul wants Christians everywhere to really know Christ (2 v
2-3). He knows this will encourage and unite them.

I've been to churches in Britain, Europe, America and Southeast Asia
and, despite their differences, knowing Jesus is what they have in
common. Jesus unites believers.

WATCH OUT!   **Read Colossians 2 v 4**

6 What is the warning in verse 4?

There will be people who can talk a good talk, and could lead Christians
away from the truth. For example, someone might say: "Jesus is
important, but he's not the most important person you should listen to".

7 Can you think of any "fine-sounding arguments" that might deceive
Christians?

That's why prayer and teaching are so important. Paul doesn't want any
Christian to be deceived and wander away from the truth, which is the
good news about Jesus.

D ABSENT AND PRESENT   **Read Colossians 2 v 5**

8 What is encouraging about the Colossians?

9 How is Paul present with them even when he's not there in person? What do you think that means?

All believers are connected by the God's Spirit. The Holy Spirit lives in all Christians, unites them and points them to Jesus.

> I travelled to Poland when I was 14. We visited a family in a Bible College my Dad had heard of. We'd never met, but they invited us in.
> We ate with them, and stayed with them—united because of Jesus.

When we hear of Christians around the world standing firm in difficult times, we rejoice. When we hear of Christians being persecuted for their faith, we weep with them and pray for them. We are united in Christ.

10 Do you know of Christians around the world you could pray for and encourage in some way?

Your church may have partners who you could find out about and pray for, write to or support. Why not make a plan to do that this week?

E CONTINUE IN HIM   **Read Colossians 2 v 6-7**

These verses are considered to be the key verses of the whole book. We could do a whole study just on these! Understanding them could transform our Christian life.

11 How does verse 6 begin? Why do you think Paul starts that way?

12 How did the Colossians become Christians in the first place (v 6)?

13 What does it mean for Jesus to be Christ?

14 What does it mean for Jesus to be Lord?

When we become a Christian, we receive Jesus as:
• **Christ**, God's chosen one who came to die in our place.
• **Lord**, the one who is now in control of our lives—we live for him.

15 There are five things Christians are to continue doing (in the table below). Can you think of things that could help you do them?

What are they to do?	What does this mean? How can you do it?
Live in him (some Bible versions say "walk in him") (v 6)	
Rooted in him (v 7)	
Built up in him (v 7)	
Strengthened in the faith as you were taught (v 7)	
Overflowing with thankfulness (v 7)	

Some people start out excited by the good news of Jesus, but as time passes they move on. They might think: "When I became a Christian, I believed Jesus was God, and his death was important. Now I'm older, I think living a good life will please God."

Paul would say: "Whoa! As you received Jesus, keep going". You became a Christian when you understood you were a sinner and knew Jesus died so you could be forgiven. That NEVER changes; NEVER forget that; NOTHING is more important. Keep rooted in Jesus and you will keep growing as a Christian.

STOP AND THINK

Are you ever tempted to believe there's something better or more important, something that you're missing out on?

What encourages you from Colossians 2 v 6-7?

PRAYER TIME

◆ What can you do to stay "rooted" in Jesus?

◆ Can you think of two specific things you could do this week?

◆ Why not pray about that now?

MEMORY VERSE

"So then, just as you received Christ Jesus as Lord, continue to live your lives in him, ROOTED AND BUILT UP in him, strengthened in the faith as you were taught, and overflowing with thankfulness."

Colossians 2 v 6-7

See what God has done

Today's Bible section: Colossians chapter 2, verses 8-15

A GETTING DISTRACTED?

❶ What distracts you or tempts you to move on from Jesus?

___ friends   ___ boyfriends

___ the message of the Bible seems hard

___ TV/internet/music   ___ family

___ friends have different opinions

___ living as a Christian is tough   ___ something else

It can be hard to keep going. There are many things that try and pull us away from Jesus.

Remember the memory verse from the last study? (It's on page 32 if you don't.) "Stay rooted in Jesus"—sometimes that's easier said than done.

Sometimes we worry we're not a very good Christian and are tempted to give up. Sometimes we think, if we just had a new experience or a special message, then it would reassure us. We'd be ok. We'd keep going.

Paul has an important message for Christians who need encouragement to keep going in their faith: *Remember Jesus.*

B REMEMBER JESUS   **Read Colossians 2 v 8**

❷ What's the warning in verse 8?

❸ What would you think if you heard someone had been taken captive?

It's not good! You're held against your will and restricted in what you can do. Verse 8 seems complicated—but the key thing Paul is saying is: "Don't be taken in. Don't be deceived by things that are not all about Jesus."

Sometimes there's teaching in churches that sounds good, but isn't rooted in Jesus.

For example:

If you're a *real* Christian you'll be at church twice a day.

If you're a *real* Christian you'll have amazing supernatural experiences.

They might sound good, but if they're just about making us feel good, (or making us feel bad if we don't manage them!), we need to watch out! A real Christian lives as Colossians 2 v 6-7 tells us. That might mean you want to go to church twice a day, but it's not a rule.

Read Colossians 2 v 9-10

❹ Why should we keep our focus on Jesus? (There are three things mentioned.) Why are they so great?

1)

2)

3)

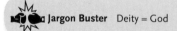 Jargon Buster   Deity = God

Just think about those three things for a moment:

Jesus was God on earth, in a body. Sometimes I'm asked: "Have you seen God?" My answer is: "No, but if I'd been born 2000 years ago I could have". Jesus was **ALL** the fullness of God in a human body.

> **We are given fullness in Christ**—we have been given everything we need. We have everything we need to know God now and for ever.

2

> **Jesus Christ is head of everything**: nothing, no one, nowhere is outside of HIS authority. NOTHING compares to Jesus.

3

So why listen to other teachings or look for a new experience? Look to JESUS.

STOP for a minute...

5 Write down your response to verses 9-10. How does this encourage you and help you to keep going forward?

C **MADE ALIVE IN JESUS**   **Read Colossians 2 v 11-13**

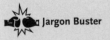 **Jargon Buster** Circumcision = what God commanded Abraham to do in Genesis 17 as a sign of belonging to his chosen people. This sign is cutting off a small piece of skin.

6 Circumcision was a physical cutting. What has been circumcised/cut off in us?

7 How have Christians been circumcised (v 11)?

Through Jesus' death and resurrection, our old sinful self died and we have been raised to new life in Jesus.

8 Did you notice the contrasts in verses 12-13?

Having been _____ *with him...*

you were also _____ *with him (v 12).*

When you were _____ *in your sins...*

God made you _____ *with Christ (v 13).*

Without physically being crucified with Jesus, we share in his death. And we share in what it achieved—our sins forgiven. We were dead, and now we're alive. Amazing!

Read Colossians 2 v 13-15

9 What stopped us knowing God and had to be cancelled (v 14)? What do you think that is?

What a mouthful! Verse 14 in the ESV Bible says: "cancelling the record of debt that stood against us with its legal demands".

"Record of debt" isn't money we owe, but a record of sin. A list of all the things we've done against God—times we've ignored him, wronged him, offended him, let him down, either on purpose, by accident or when we didn't even know we were doing it!

> **Think about the last week. Have you...**
>
> • gossiped about someone?
>
> • been jealous/judgmental of others?
>
> • hurt others with words or actions?
>
> • put God first in everything?
>
> • lived as Jesus would have lived?

🔟 What has God done through Jesus' death on the cross (v 14-15)?

Sin separates us from God, and must be dealt with. Jesus has done it. We were dead and now we are alive. All because of Jesus.

D STOP AND THINK

Don't be deceived by people who tell you there's something better than Jesus (v 8). It's all about what God has done through Jesus. Keep fixed on him.

When you're feeling low as a Christian—*remember Jesus.*

When your sin weighs you down—*remember Jesus.*

When you're struggling with difficulties or sadness—*remember Jesus.*

When life is great—*keep your eyes on Jesus.*

There is no one better, no one greater. Stay rooted in him, built up in him. You were dead and he has made you alive.

PRAYER TIME

Try some "Teaspoon prayers" (TSP):

THANK God that through Jesus your sinful nature has been cut off.

SAY SORRY to God for the things that get in the way of your relationship with him.

PRAISE him that he has triumphed over sin and death.

You have Jesus

Today's Bible section: Colossians chapter 2, verses 16-23

A YOU vs. OTHERS

- Do you ever compare yourself with *other people*? Maybe you think: "I wish I had her figure, hair, clothes or intelligence" or "I wish I was as confident as her, or as popular".

- Do you ever compare yourself with *other Christians*? It can leave us feeling rubbish. We worry we're a useless Christian; that we're not as good at praying, or talking to friends, or living a godly life as others.

- Have you ever been tempted to *forget* about the whole thing?

- Maybe you're not a Christian, but you see other Christians and *can't imagine* how you'd ever be like them.

Paul has reassuring advice as he gives a serious warning in today's passage.

B BEWARE THE JUDGMENTAL PERSON   Read Colossians 2 v 16-17

❶ Paul starts verse 16 with a "therefore", so we need to look back at the previous verses. What did Paul remind the Colossians of in chapter 2 v 9-15?

❷ What's the warning in verse 16?

> The Jews followed rules and regulations, had foods they couldn't eat, and festivals they celebrated. These were given by God to help them keep focusing on him as their God and Father, and to point them forward to something better.

3 How are these things described in verse 17?

4 Why weren't these things important any more?

Imagine you discover a cousin living far away who you've never met. You email, exchanging life stories and photos and get on well. One day she emails and says she's coming to visit. You're excited and plan things you'll do together. But when she arrives, you don't look at her—you just keep looking at the photo. When she talks to you, you email a reply. That's ridiculous, isn't it? The reality is that she's here with you, and yet you're trying to communicate with her in the old way. You're missing out on having a face-to-face relationship.

Don't let anyone stop you missing out on the reality of a relationship with Jesus (v 17). Jesus has come. You can have a relationship with him and speak to him directly.

But there's another warning...

BEWARE THE "SUPER-HOLY PERSON"   **Read Colossians 2 v 18-19**

5 Who else should the Colossians beware?

6 What is Paul worried might happen (v 18)?

7 How might people disqualify them for the prize?

So what were these people like? Rather than getting bogged down in the detail, let's get to the heart of the problem.

8 What is the BIG problem with the person in verses 18b-19a?

They seem to delight in trying to be "super-holy".

Maybe...

> they boast about getting up at 5am to have a super-long time reading their Bible
>
> *or*
>
> they say if you haven't had a picture or a vision from God, you're not a real Christian
>
> *or*
>
> they boast about how many times they've been to church in the last month, and how many Christian books they've read.

They sound "super-holy" and can leave you feeling there's something missing from your relationship with God, if you're not like them.

Paul says: "Don't let anyone disqualify you". Being a Christian isn't about "doing things". It's about being in Christ; being connected to the head (v 19).

Sometimes you can get so "super-holy" you push God out of the picture altogether—doing lots of great things, but forgetting about Jesus! Make sure that's not you.

9 If Jesus is the head, what are we (v 19)?

10 So why can no one disqualify us from the prize?

D **RULES AND REGULATIONS**   **Read Colossians 2 v 20-23**

11 What does Paul remind them of in verse 20?

12 What's the challenge in verses 20-21?

13 What is the problem with rules (v 22-23)?

Christians have been forgiven by Jesus and freed from sin, so we shouldn't go back to following rules. When Paul says: "They lack any value in restraining sensual indulgence", it's a fancy way of saying that, although rules can appear wise, they don't change the human heart. The problem of sin is much deeper than something that's solved by simply obeying new rules.

For example: the Bible says sex outside of marriage isn't right. It's not how God intended sex to be enjoyed. You could obey that rule because you think it will make you a good Christian—but actually you really want to break it, because you fancy your boyfriend and you want to be with him. Having the rule won't change your heart. Keeping the rule won't make you love Jesus more.

But if you know that you have died with Christ—and recognise how much he loves you, and what he's done for you—suddenly this doesn't seem like a rule just to stop you enjoying life. Instead it's a way of life that pleases God. He shows us how to understand and enjoy his good gifts in the best possible way.

D STOP AND THINK

It's easy to compare ourselves with other people, rather than with the head, Jesus.

14 In what circumstances are you in danger of comparing yourself with others (either positively or negatively)?

PRAYER TIME

Say sorry for times you've tried to do things to impress God, and pushed Jesus out.

Thank God that knowing him is not about obeying rules, but being forgiven.

Others: pray that the way you live will show others that "it's all about Jesus".

Pray that God will help you to love him more, and want to live the way he says is best.

MEMORY VERSE

"...the head [Jesus] from whom the whole body ... grows as GOD CAUSES it to grow."

Colossians 2 v 19

Look up   Solo

Today's Bible section: Colossians chapter 3, verses 1-4

A WHERE'S YOUR LIFE GOING?

❶ Where do you see yourself in 10, 20 or 30 years' time?

Paul challenges Christians to think carefully about where they're going, and what they're setting their hearts and minds on.

B PAST   **Read Colossians 3 v 1-4**

❷ What three things have happened for Christians (v 1 and v 3)?

1)

2)

3)

Sound familiar? Flick back to Colossians 2 v 12, 13 and 20 as a reminder.

God raised Jesus from the dead, and all our sins are forgiven. We've been raised with Jesus too. That's the power of God! If you're a Christian, you died; your old life, lived in rebellion against God, has gone; and you are raised to new life, now and for all eternity.

❸ What does that mean to you? Why not write a prayer of response to God, thanking him for what he's done for you?

> If you're not sure that you understand/believe this for yourself yet, why not write down a question and ask it in the next session?

C   PRESENT   **Re-read Colossians 3 v 1-2**

❹ What does Paul tell us we are to do (v 1-2)?

Some Bible translations say "seek" rather than "set" (eg: "Seek the things that are above").

❺ What does that mean?

> We set our hearts on many things. Once my heart was set on being a princess. "Sarah" means "princess" so I thought I had a chance (that's six-year-old logic for you!). Sadly, I needed to marry a prince and there weren't many(!) in my area. I thought about it lots but nothing happened.

We usually worry about and concentrate on things we set our hearts on.
- Getting the right grades, so we get a good job.
- Meeting someone, being liked, so we can get married.
- Being good enough to achieve certain goals.

These aren't bad things, but Paul says: *"Set your hearts on things above"*.

Because we've been raised with Christ, we need to look to him in all things.

You wouldn't get in a car, start the engine, put your foot on the accelerator, then turn and look out the back window while driving forwards. You look where you're going.

6 Why do we set our hearts on things above (v 1 and v 4)?

Hebrews 10 v 12 says:
"But when this priest had offered for all time one sacrifice for sins, he sat down at the right hand of God."

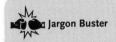 **Jargon Buster**   Sacrifice = the Jews offered animals to die in their place to deal with their sin. A sacrifice was a death/offering in the place of a human life.

7 When did the priest (Jesus) sit down?

8 Colossians 3 v 1 says that Jesus is "seated at the right hand of God". What can we be sure of?

Re-read Colossians 3 v 3-4

9 Do you ever have days when being a Christian is a struggle and you feel as if you've let God down?

10 What does Paul tell us about our life now (v 3)?

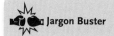
We can be confident that we're forgiven— it won't always be obvious, and we won't always feel it, but be assured, your life is hidden safe with God.

11 How can you set your heart and mind on things above?

SCENARIOS

How will that help in these situations?

You have important exams. Everyone's talking about how much work they need to do. *How can you set your mind on things above (and not just on the results you might get) as you prepare for the exams?*

Some of your friends have boyfriends—they're "in love" and tell you it's amazing. They think you should go out with someone too. The people they suggest aren't Christians. There are Christian boys at church, but you aren't attracted to any of them. *How can you set your mind on things above and not just on having a boyfriend?*

You're good at tennis. You play in a weekend club and more matches and training sessions are being fixed for a Sunday morning. Pressure is being put on you to play. You love tennis, but want to be part of your church and youth group. *How can you set your mind on things above and not just on playing tennis?*

To set our minds on things above we need to listen to God—in his word, the Bible. God will guide and help us to live in the present, confident of the past and preparing for the future.

D **FURE**   **Re-read Colossians 3 v 4**

12 What will happen in the future?

You died, you have been raised and you WILL appear in glory with Christ. If you're a Christian, and so know you've been forgiven by God, you can be certain of that.

13 How does that give us confidence now?

We work, study, make friends, get married, travel, play sports, develop skills. They're all good—but we should do them with our eyes set firmly on where we're going, living as people who will one day have their "real" lives revealed.

Where are your eyes set—on life now or on Jesus, who forgave your sin, and has raised you for life with him for ever?

PRAYER TIME

Thank God that Jesus' death means that our sin can be fully forgiven.

Ask him to help you to keep your eyes fixed on him.

Talk to him about areas in your life where your eyes are fixed on earthly things rather than on heavenly things.

Live the life

Today's Bible section: Colossians chapter 3, verses 5-11

A LIVE THE LIFE

1 If you met someone who was training for the Olympics, what would their life look like?

2 If you met someone who wanted to be a famous singer, what would their life look like?

Training, practising, working hard—preparing to be the person they want to be in the future.

> In the first four verses of chapter 3, Paul reminded us of the life Christians have: a life hidden with Christ. One day we will live the life Jesus intended. For now we're living and growing as God's people, with a future goal in sight—being with Jesus for ever.
>
> And Paul says this changes how we live now...

B CHANGE OF LIFE   Read Colossians 3 v 5-7

3 What are we to do with things that belong to our earthly nature? Why is it so final?

4 What are we to put to death (v 5)?

They're mostly linked to sex... Maybe you think: "Surprise, surprise. Christians always seems to go on about sex: 'You can't, you shouldn't, you mustn't'. Is it really such a big deal?"

5 Who created sex and what did he think of it? (Read Genesis 1 v 28, 31.)

Sexual immorality takes God's gift of sex and uses it in a self-centred and self-serving way. *Lust, evil desires* and *greed* can all lead to sexual immorality and *impurity*—and people get hurt. It's not God's best.

God is not anti-sex. He created sex, and enjoyed in marriage in the way he intended it's brilliant! But like many things, when we ignore God's instructions, we spoil the gifts he's given us. So Paul says put wrong sexual thoughts and actions to death.

6 Why should the sex life of a Christian be different from those around them (v 3, 7)?

7 Does Paul think the Colossians can change (v 7)?

C GET RID   **Read Colossians 3 v 8**

8 What else are Christians to get rid of?

49

9 Can you explain all the words in verse 8?

  • anger:

  • rage:

  • malice:

  • slander:

  • filthy language:

10 What's the link between all of these things?

Our new life in Christ affects our sex life (what we do with our bodies, v 5) and it affects how we speak to one another (what we say with our mouths, v 8).

11 Why does Paul say they must get rid of the things in verse 8 too?

⓬ How do verses 9 and 11 remind us that living as a Christian isn't something we have to do on our own?

As we put these things to death—get rid of them from our lives—we're doing it with other Christians. We can help each other to do this, more and more.

⓭ How does verse 10 show that the change will be gradual rather than instant?

> Getting rid of sin is something we should want to do; sin doesn't fit with our new life.
>
> Day by day, Christians are becoming more like their Creator, but it will be hard and will take time. Amazingly, we're doing it in God's power, and with the help of Christian brothers and sisters (more of that in the next study).

⓮ What do all the people in verse 11 have in common?

PRAYER TIME

Are there specific things that you do with your body or say with your mouth that you need to put to death? Are there things in your life that don't fit with the new life you live?

- *Sleeping with your boyfriend*
- *Thinking about/using sex in the wrong way*
- *Looking at porn on the internet/in magazines*
- *Reading magazines/books that make you lust*
- *Flirting/treating boys as objects—playing with their feelings and emotions*
- *Being jealous of people who have the relationship you would like*
- *Getting angry with friends, parents, teachers...*
- *Gossiping*
- *Lying*
- *Swearing; using God's name in a wrong way*
- *Unkind and nasty talk*

Pray that God will help you to "put them to death" and that he will "renew" you in his image.

MEMORY VERSE

"... since you have taken off your OLD SELF with its practices and have put on the NEW SELF"

Colossians 3 v 9-10

New clothes Solo

Today's Bible section: Colossians chapter 3, verses 12-17

A FAVOURITE CLOTHES

❶ Have you got a favourite piece of clothing? Something that always makes you feel good? A hoodie, pair of jeans, pair of shoes? It doesn't matter how old and battered they get—you love them.

❷ If you had loads of money, what piece of clothing would you rush out and buy?

❸ If you had to throw five or six other items out of your wardrobe to have it—would you still buy it?

In Colossians 3 v 5 we were told to "put to death" all the things that belong to our old way of life.

Imagine a giant wardrobe full of clothes. God is telling us to get rid of all the things that don't fit with our new lifestyle. He doesn't just help us empty the wardrobe and leave us with nothing to wear. God gives us a whole new outfit to wear, and it's better than anything we had before. We go from horrible, dirty rags to the best clothes imaginable.

Read Colossians 3 v 12-14

It's important to have the right clothes for the right kind of life. You wouldn't ride a motorbike in a bikini or sit on a tropical beach in a snow suit. It's important to dress for the life you lead.

4 If you were given new clothes, what would you do with them?

5 How are the Christians described in verse 12?

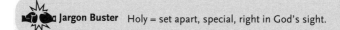 **Jargon Buster**   Holy = set apart, special, right in God's sight.

6 What's your reaction to that description?

It's pretty awesome, isn't it? Maybe you don't feel worthy. None of us are. But God chooses to love people like you and me! We don't deserve it—think about the dirty rags we bring to him (3 v 5 and v 8)—but because of Jesus' death, we've been forgiven and given amazing new clothes.

C **GET DRESSED**

7 How should God's chosen, holy and loved people be dressed?

54

8 How does that list compare with what we read in 3 v 5 and v 8?

We have a new outfit that shows we're living for Jesus.

9 What's the "coat" that we put on top of all these things (v 14)?

God's chosen people have a new outfit. One that looks out for others, cares, is kind, patient and gentle. It's one that loves others—and what an impact it makes!

There isn't room for the dirty, filthy rags we used to wear. Our wardrobes are full of the best clothes we could have! They're clothes that help us live in unity with other Christians, and be a witness to others around us (we'll see more in Colossians chapter 4).

On page 78 you'll find pictures of two tops. In the last session, Paul told us what we need to put to death/take off. In this session, we learn about our new wardrobe. You might find it helpful to write on each top to remind you what needs to go, and what amazing things we get in their place.

D STOP AND THINK

Are you wearing your new clothes?

Ask God to clothe you with these things every day, in everything you do and with everyone you meet.

E A NEW COMMUNITY

Have you ever turned up at a party or an event in the wrong clothes? Everyone else is in normal clothes and you're dressed as a superhero? Embarrassing! It's hard to fit in and enjoy yourself, isn't it? If at least one other person was dressed like you, it would make life easier.

You're not alone. All Christians have these new clothes and should encourage each other to live for Jesus.

Read Colossians 3 v 15-16

10 How does verse 15 describe Christians?

11 What word is repeated twice in this verse?

12 How will wearing our new outfit bring peace?

13 What things do Christians do together in church/youth group? (Fill in the table.)

Colossians 3 v 16	What does verse 16 say Christians will do when they're together?	How will this help us to wear our new clothes?
Let the message of Christ dwell among you richly as you teach and admonish one another with all wisdom...	1.	
	2.	
through psalms, hymns, and songs from the Spirit, singing to God with gratitude in your hearts.	3.	
	4.	

14 How is verse 17 a great summary of all we've read in chapter 3?

PRAYER TIME

Questions to ponder and turn into prayer

Have a read through these situations. Which ones do you need to talk to God about?

- Do you let the message of Christ dwell richly in your heart? Or do you forget it as soon as you leave church/youth group/one2one?

- Do you talk to your friends about what you've learned? Do you teach and admonish each other with the word you've heard?

- Do you enjoy singing in church/youth group? Do you consider how you can encourage others as you sing truths about God?

- Does your mind wander as you sing? Or do you use the opportunity to really praise and thank God for how amazing he is?

Ask God to help you put verse 17 into action:

"And whatever you do, whether in word or deed, do it all in the name of the Lord Jesus, giving thanks to God the Father through him."

Living for God (1)

Today's Bible section: Colossians chapter 3, verses 18-21

A HAPPY FAMILIES

❶ Think about married couples on TV or in films.
What impression do they give you of marriage?

Think about Christian married couples you know. What impression
do *they* give you of marriage? Is it different to the TV/films?

B I WILL! Read Colossians 3 v 18-19

You're probably not married now, but one day you might be. So thinking
about what a "godly" marriage looks like is important as you think about
if and who you could marry.

❷ Fill in what husbands and wives are to do:

Wives	Husbands
_____	_____
to your husbands	your wives

❸ What does it mean to submit?

People often think it means wives are slaves and do everything their
husband says. "Submitting" to your husband doesn't mean being
ordered around and treated as a doormat. Far from it. Do you remember
Colossians 3 v 12-17? It doesn't make sense for a husband to put on all
his new clothes and then treat his wife like a slave!

If we understand what *husbands* are to do, it will help us see what it
means to "submit". It will also help us think about who we might go out
with and marry.

4 What do you think it means for a man truly to love his wife?

Being romantic, buying flowers, saying she's beautiful! Those things are great but they're superficial. Paul has bigger things in mind when he tells husbands to love their wives. **Look at Ephesians 5 v 25.**

5 How is a husband to love his wife?

6 How did Jesus show us how much he loved us (Colossians 1 v 22)?

Jesus' love for his church is much stronger than "I love you because you're beautiful". It's "I love you, and I died so you can know God!"

It's love that even loves the unlovable: *"While we were still sinners* (very unlovable), *Christ died for us" (Romans 5 v 8).*

7 What kind of man does God want his Christian daughters to marry? (See Ephesians 5 v 25 again.)

8 So, if you're a Christian, what kind of man does God want you to go out with? (Hint: both of your answers should look similar.)

Marriage is a picture of Christ loving his church, and the church submitting to and loving Jesus. A husband loving his wife will do all he can to help her love God more.

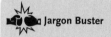

Jargon Buster Submit = to follow the godly lead. Christians submit to (follow the godly lead of) Christ. Wives submit to (follow the godly lead of) their husbands.

9 If a husband loves his wife as Christ loves the church, will it be easier to submit to him?

10 If a wife submits to her husband, will it be easier for him to love her as Christ loves the church?

SCENARIOS

- A boy who's not a Christian asks you out. How do these verses help you answer?

- A boy who says he's a Christian asks you out. He doesn't come to church all that often and says reading the Bible isn't that important. How do these verses help you answer?

Marriage isn't for everyone. But if you're a Christian and would like to get married, you need a husband (and therefore a boyfriend) who loves Jesus.

A man who:
- wants to love you, as Jesus has loved him!

- who wants to help you "live a life worthy of the Lord and please him in every way: bearing fruit in every good work, growing in the knowledge of God" (Colossians 1 v 10).

Christians are to submit to God—to live the life he's called us to. When we remember his amazing love, we'll want to submit to him as Lord and live for him.

A godly husband will be the kind of man his wife loves to submit to. Verses 18 and 19 go together. One doesn't work without the other.

To think more about the whole area of going out with someone, have a look at "What about dating?" on page 80.

C PARENTS!

Think about parents and children you see on TV or in films.

What impression do they give you of family life?

Think about your relationship with your parents/carers. What's great about it? Are there things that are hard?

Paul mentions fathers. That doesn't mean mothers don't matter—of course they do! But, as men love their wives, and treat their children right, wives who submit to their husbands will do the same.

Read Colossians 3 v 20-21

⑪ What are children and fathers to do?

Children	Fathers
_____	_____
your parents in everything	your children

⑫ What do you think when you hear the word "obey"?

We like to be our own boss. We don't like people telling us what to do. But Colossians 3 v 20 says: "Obey your parents".

⑬ Why should we obey them? What does that mean?

⑭ Do you usually obey your parents? Why?
    Is it for the reason that Paul commands?

SCENARIOS

What will it look like to obey your parents in these situations?

- You're ready to go out, but when you come downstairs, your parents look at what you're wearing and send you to change before you go out? How do you react?

- Your parents, who aren't Christians, say you can't go to church because they want you to spend time with them on a Sunday. What should you do?

15 What are fathers commanded (v 21)?

16 Would it be easier to obey a parent who was doing this?

If you constantly disobey your parents, it makes it harder for them to encourage and love you as they need to.

17 Does your relationship with your parents/carers need to change?

Paul talks about relationships in pairs. Both sides need to do what's described for the relationship to work in the way God intended.

PRAYER TIME

Thank God for the important people in your life who help you love him more.

Say sorry for specific relationships, attitudes and situations where you haven't lived as God says.

Pray that God will be the centre of all your relationships.

Session 12 Living for God (2)

Today's Bible section: Colossians chapter 3 v 22 to 4 v 1

❶ What do you want to be when you're older?

When you were little, did you want to be a princess? And then maybe a nurse or a teacher or a mother? Or even an engineer or an astronaut? They're jobs we often play at when we're young... but then reality hits! You have to choose your options, then college courses or what job to apply for, and it can all get a bit complicated.

Paul is concerned about work—but not so much with what job we do but *how* we do it.

A WORKING AS A SLAVE   Read Colossians 3 v 22 – 4 v 1

❷ What do you think of when you hear the word slave?

There were slaves in the Colossian church, but not in the way we think of them. We probably think in negative terms, remembering the awful slave trade that ended in the 19th century.

Slaves were common when Paul was writing. But they had much more status and respect than we might imagine. They also had the opportunity to gain their freedom.

Paul has a message specifically for them in this letter. They were included. They were part of the church family!

3 Fill in what slaves and masters were to do:

Slaves	Masters
_____ your earthly masters (3 v 22)	_____ your slaves with what is right and fair (4 v 1)

B **EARTHLY MASTERS**   **Read Colossians 3 v 22**

4 How are the owners of the slaves described? Why?

5 How might a slave be tempted to behave (v 22)?

6 How *should* they live?

There's no excuse for slaves to say: "Now I'm a Christian, I don't have to obey my earthly master. I only have to obey God." Obeying God will mean they also obey their earthly masters.

You can't claim to be a follower of Jesus, but ignore or reject people who have authority over you. One of the ways we show that Jesus is Lord of our lives is by living for him in everything.

7 Paul is writing to slaves, but how does verse 23 apply to all of us? (Does this remind you of a verse from a previous session?)

8 Can you think of examples of what it might look like for you...

• at school?

• in a job?

• at home?

9 What reason does verse 24 give for us "working for the Lord, not for human masters"?

Slaves may have had limited freedom because of their status, but they were totally free in Jesus—free to live for him and serve him in everything.

They may not have had many rewards or perks to look forward to in this life, but they had the most amazing inheritance promised to them.

10 What is the amazing reward promised? (Look back at chapter 1 v 12 and 3 v 4. Where will we be one day?)

As you live your life—at home, at school, at work—do you think that you're serving Christ?

Would other people know that from the way that you act, speak and live?

E **WATCH OUT**   **Read Colossians 3 v 25 – 4 v 1**

11 What's the warning in verse 25?

12 Masters are given just one instruction. Look back to question 3 to remind yourself of what it is (4 v 1)?

13 What might masters in a position of power have been tempted to do?

14 Why shouldn't masters do that (v 25)?

Over the last two studies, Paul has given instructions to husbands and wives, parents and children, and slaves and masters.

⓯ Each person has a role to play... Looking back at these verses, what is the big thing that each of them needs to remember?

• Chapter 3 v 18b:

• Chapter 3 v 20b:

• Chapter 3 v 23:

• Chapter 4 v 1b:

⓰ What's your attitude to work? What's your attitude to people in authority over you? Is it like 3 v 23 or is it more like the slave who isn't working with all their heart (3 v 22)?

PRAYER TIME

"Whatever you do, work at it with all your heart, as working for the Lord, not for human masters."

Pray that God would help you to make this the aim of your life.

Do you need to ask for God's help to change your attitude at school, in a job you have, and as you live at home?

Get talking

Today's Bible section: Colossians chapter 4, verses 2-6

A WHO ARE YOU TALKING TO?

❶ Do you like talking? Who to? What about?

> Often women love to talk. People often say women speak more than men. I found a statistic that said women speak around 20,000 words a day, and men only 7000! That may not be true, but when we're with close friends or family members we can talk for hours and hours. Sometimes our conversation is good; sometimes not so good.
>
> Paul has something to say about who we talk to. He has much more in mind than a girly catch-up with a bar of chocolate!

B TALK TO GOD ABOUT PEOPLE   **Read Colossians 4 v 2-4**

❷ What's the instruction in verse 2?

❸ What does it means to be devoted?

We can be devoted to many things. We can be very devoted to talking. But are we devoted to talking to God in prayer?

❹ Why does Paul say "be watchful"? (Colossians 2 v 8, 16 might help!)

5 Why can the Colossians be thankful (Colossians 1 v 21-22, 3 v 1)?

6 What else does Paul ask them to pray for (v 3)?

7 Where is Paul as he writes this letter (v 3)?

8 Does his prayer surprise you?

It's incredible. Paul's in prison because he's been talking about Jesus. He neither prays for his release nor shuts up! He wants to talk to people about Jesus, even when he's in chains. So Paul asks the Colossians to pray that a door would be opened for the message—not the door to the prison, but the door to the hearts of people who don't know Jesus.

9 How important does Paul think prayer is?

10 How does Paul want to speak to people (v 4)?

Prayer is essential. It's important that the Colossians talk to God, praying for people who don't know Jesus, and praying they'd hear the truth and respond.

C STOP AND THINK!

You talk to a lot of different people in a day.

- Do you talk to God regularly?
- Do you talk to him about people who don't know him?
- Do you pray they'd listen and want to know more?
- Is there someone you'd like to know Jesus? Why not stop and pray for them now? You could write their name in this box:

D TALK TO PEOPLE ABOUT GOD　　　Read Colossians 4 v 5-6

Paul urges the Colossians to talk to people about God.

It's great to sit in your bedroom and pray for your friends to know Jesus, but if you never actually talk about him, it will make it harder for them!

⓫ Do you find it easy to talk about Jesus with friends who don't know him?

What makes it hard?

What makes is easier?

It's the most important message they'll every hear, but sometimes we do find it hard. Verses 5-6 should encourage us:

⓬ Does Paul say that you need to be able to...

preach a sermon? ✓ ✗

lead a Bible study? ✓ ✗

explain every detail of Jesus' life, death and resurrection? ✓ ✗

🔞 What should Christians do (v 5-6)?

Verse 5a: _____

Look back at chapter 3. Remember who you are in Christ, and the new wardrobe you have.

① How will that help you to be wise?

1

Verse 5b: _____

② Can you think of any opportunities that you have to talk about Jesus?

I don't think Paul expected the Colossians to go out and preach on the streets. He called them to pray for opportunities, and then make the most of them. If someone asks, TELL THEM!

2

Verse 6: _____

③ What does it mean for your conversation to be...

full of grace?

seasoned with salt?

3

I guarantee that as you talk to people about God, you'll make a mess of it sometimes. You'll say the wrong thing, some people won't like it and some people won't be interested. But keep going! God loves us to talk about him, and there *will* be people who see how you live, hear what you say and want to know more.

⓮ Before we talk to people what are we to do (4 v 2)?

> It all starts with God. As we're devoted to him, and talking to him, he'll equip us to live for him and speak for him.

⓯ Does it say anywhere in these verses that it's our responsibility to make people Christians?

⓰ What *are* we called to do?

God will do the rest! That's something worth praising him for now!

PRAYER TIME

Thank God that he's the one who changes people.

Pray that you'll make the most of every opportunity you have to talk about Jesus. If you don't get many opportunities, pray for more!

What opportunities will you have in the next few weeks to talk about Jesus? Why not make a note of them here?

If you're not yet a Christian, pray that you'll have opportunities to ask more questions and that God will help you see who he is.

MEMORY VERSE:

"Be WISE in the way you act toward outsiders; make the most of EVERY opportunity."

Colossians 4 v 5

In this together

Today's Bible section: Colossians chapter 4 v 7-18

A GETTING STARTED

❶ Write down the three people who've been the biggest encouragement to you in your life so far, and why.

We need other people. Life can be miserable when you're on your own. If I was ever marooned on a desert island, the solitude and loneliness would be the worst thing. Even worse than any spiders or bugs! I'd hate having no one to talk to and enjoy being with.

B PEOPLE MATTER   Read Colossians 4 v 7-18

This might seem an odd way to end the letter—and it might be tempting to skim over what Paul says and who he mentions. We don't know the people he names, so why does it matter?

But wait a minute... read it, look at the questions and see if you can work out why these last few verses are so encouraging.

❷ How many different people does Paul mention in these verses?

❸ Who is delivering the letter to the Colossians?

4 How are they described?

5 How does Paul describe the people in verses 7, 9, 10 and 11?

• verse 7:

• verse 9:

• verse 10:

• verse 11:

6 What does that tell us about his relationship with them?

7 How many of them send greetings to the Colossians?
What does this tell us?

8 Are the people Paul mentions Jews or Gentiles (v 10-11)?
Why is that important (3 v 11)?

9 Who was Epaphras (1 v 7)?
What is he doing and why (4 v 12-13)?

10 Who is Paul concerned about as he sends the letter (v 15-17)?

11 So, what do these verses tell us about Paul, his ministry and his relationships with other Christians?

Paul loved people, and had a lot of time for them.
He didn't just want people to become Christians but also to be strong and mature in the Lord.

STOP AND THINK

Do you care about God's people like that? Do you love to be with and encourage other Christians in your church, youth group, and those further away?

How can you learn from Paul's example?

PRAYER TIME

Give thanks for the people who challenge and encourage you.

Pray that you would love and encourage others.

Try and pray for some people by name.

D **THE END**

12 Make time to sit down and read the whole of Colossians in one go (that is how letters are meant to be read!).

As you read, write down...

• great things about Jesus

• great things about following Jesus

• things that you know need to change in your life to help you be more like Jesus.

⓭ What's the one big thing that you're going to remember from the book of Colossians?

MEMORY VERSE

"So then, just as you RECEIVED CHRIST JESUS as Lord, continue to live your lives in him,
      ROOTED AND BUILT UP in him,
            strengthened in the faith as you were taught,
and OVERFLOWING WITH THANKFULNESS."

Colossians 2 v 6-7

PUT TO DEATH, therefore, whatever belongs to your earthly nature...

sexual immorality
impurity, lust
evil desires
o greed
anger
rage
malice
slander
filthy
language

Colossians 3 v 5, 8

As God's chosen people, holy and dearly loved, **CLOTHE YOURSELVES** with... Compassion, Kindness, humility, gentleness + patience, forgive + bear with one another

ABOVE ALL THESE VIRTUES PUT ON LOVE, binding them together in unity

Colossians 3 v 12-14   79

HAPPILY EVER AFTER?

I'm guessing you've watched a chick flick or two! Boy meets girl, girl falls in love with boy, boy isn't interested, but something happens, and he finally realises he's actually in love with her and they live happily ever after.

Or rather the film ends as they finally get together—but we never really find out what happens. Do they break up two years later? Do they get married? Do they have kids? Do they get on? Do they row a lot?

I think sometimes we separate dating and marriage more than we realise. We can get so excited by the thought of dating that we forget that it can lead to marriage.

You'd probably like to get married one day—and if you're a Christian you probably think marrying another Christian is a good idea—but all that seems a long way off at the moment. You read Colossians 3 v 18 and you think: "Great, I'll think about that more when I'm older".

THE PERFECT BOYFRIEND

The Bible doesn't really say anything about dating as it just didn't happen back then. Their culture was very different from ours. But the Bible does say a lot about relationships.

Going out with someone, spending time with someone you really like, and who really likes you, can be great. It's lovely being with someone who wants to listen to you, and make you feel special. But is there more than that?

What sort of boy are you interested in? Are you thinking about what they look like? What they like doing? Whether they're funny, or sporty, or fun to be with? Whether they love and follow Jesus?

Thinking carefully about the people we spend time with is important; our friends influence us and affect what we're like. Having friends is brilliant—but building friendships takes time, as we spend time together and sharing things.

Important people in our lives support and encourage us, and we support and help them too. This is true of friendships, and boyfriends. They're special to us, we want to please them, and care for them and do things that make them happy. They're important.

WHAT MATTERS MOST?

In Matthew 6 v 19-23 Jesus says:

> "Do not store up for yourselves treasures on earth, where moths and vermin destroy, and where thieves break in and steal. But store up for yourselves treasures in heaven, where moths and vermin do not destroy, and where thieves do not break in and steal. For where your treasure is, there your heart will be also."

These verses warn us against having earthly treasures—about treating things on earth as more important than Jesus. It's so easy to do that with a boyfriend. Having a boyfriend can become more important than following Jesus, and that can lead to building a relationship with someone who isn't going to help us love Jesus more.

TWO DANGERS

There are two big dangers if you go out with someone who isn't a growing, committed Christian. One danger is that your treasure changes. Instead of loving Jesus as your number one, your boyfriend becomes your treasure, and your relationship with him becomes more important than Jesus. Gradually you drift away from following Jesus.

Another danger is that if you're a Christian and you love Jesus, but your boyfriend doesn't, he'll get upset and be jealous that Jesus is your treasure, your number one, instead of him. That won't be helpful in a relationship or in growing as a Christian.

However, if you're both Christians, if you both love Jesus, if he's your number one and you both want to love God more and more and be more like him—he will be your focus. You'll be committed to helping each other love and serve God more.

KEEP ROOTED IN JESUS

My Christian friends are very important to me. They help me keep living as a Christian, they pray for me and with me. They encourage me to keep going and remind me of who Jesus is and what he's done (and I do the same for them.)

My boyfriend (and potential future husband) should be my best friend. What's the best type of friend? One who shares my passion for Jesus, who wants to keep going and growing, and wants me to do the same.

Colossians 2 v 6-7 says:

> "So then, just as you received Christ Jesus as Lord, continue to live your lives in him, rooted and built up in him, strengthened in the faith as you were taught, and overflowing with thankfulness."

Just as you received Christ Jesus as Lord, continue, keep rooted in him. If you're rooted in Jesus, and want to follow him, but your boyfriend's roots are somewhere else, you'll be growing in different directions.

If you're going out with a Christian and you're both rooted in Jesus, you'll grow together and help each other to love God more and more.

You may not be thinking about getting married yet, but don't separate your dating from marriage. What you do now affects what happens in the future.

If you think it doesn't matter, you may find yourself in a relationship where Jesus just doesn't feature. You may end up drifting away from Jesus.

NOT YOUR HUSBAND

In Colossians 3 v 5 Paul says we should put to death sexual immorality, impurity and lust. These things don't belong to the Christian life. They don't belong with the new set of clothes we've been given.

Treating your boyfriend as if he's your husband when he's not is a bad idea. One day he may be your husband, but he may be someone else's. Unless you've said "I will", he isn't your husband.

Sex outside of marriage is not God's best. Sleeping with your boyfriend may feel wonderful, it may feel "right", but it won't help you love Jesus more. It won't help either of you to follow Jesus if you know that you're taking his precious gift and using it in the wrong way.

You may have met a godly Christian boy, and you're helping each other to love Jesus more, and it's great. Colossians 3 v 18 says: "Wives submit to your husbands", so maybe you're wondering whether that applies to you too. Paul is clear that he's talking to wives and husbands. So the answer is no, because your boyfriend is not your husband.

Women are to submit to Jesus, their parents and their husband—not every man they're in a relationship with. But, you need to consider if your boyfriend is someone you could submit to.

Is he willing to love you as Christ loved the church? Because if you get married, you're called to submit to him. If he isn't a loving, godly boyfriend, he'll struggle to be a loving, godly husband, and he won't be a man you can submit to.

IN JESUS AND FOR JESUS

In all your relationships, especially ones that are so close and important, make sure you:

- keep rooted in Jesus (Colossians 2 v 6-7).

- clothe yourself as the person God has made you (Colossians 3 v 12).

- live for Jesus in all you do (Colossians 3 v 17).

Keep praying that your relationships will help you to do these things, and will help you love Jesus more.

To help you tell your friends about Jesus...
www.christianityexplored.org

The Christianity Explored
website is like a toolbox,
equipping you to talk to people you know about Jesus.
And you can point your friends to it too, so that
they can keep finding out more about Christianity
themselves. It features:

• answers to tough questions.
• a visual outline explaining what Christianity is.
• real-life stories of people's experiences of becoming
  Christians.

Why not take a look?

To help show your friends who Jesus is...
one2one: Just Looking

If you know someone who's really interested in what you believe, the best thing you can do is get them reading God's word!

That's what one of the books in this one2one range is designed to do. *Just Looking* makes it easy for you and a friend to look at the Gospel of Luke in the New Testament, so that they, and you, can come face to face with Jesus, and discover who he is, why he came, and why he matters to all of us.

You can order a copy (or two) here:

www.thegoodbook.co.uk/
one2one-just-looking (UK)

www.thegoodbook.com/
one2one-just-looking (US)

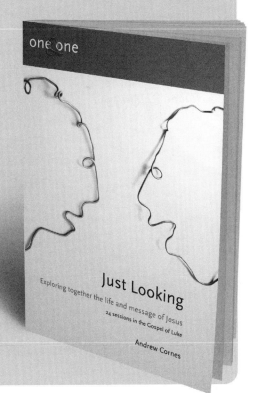

one2one

Just Looking

Exploring together the life and message of Jesus
24 sessions in the Gospel of Luke

Andrew Cornes

Living for Jesus today

Helping you read, understand and apply the Bible

HERO *by Jonty Allcock*

Discover what happens when God takes hold of loser-boy Gideon and moulds him into the unlikeliest of heroes...

LOST *by Jonty Allcock*

In the deceptively simple story of the lost son, Jesus gets to the heart of what it means to be lost to God, and found by him again.

TRUE *by Sarah Bradley*

A book to help 11 to 14-year-old girls become excited about living for Jesus in every relationship in their lives—God, church, friends, parents, boys, non-Christians and the world.

thegoodbook

COMPANY

Opening up the Bible

At The Good Book Company, we are dedicated to helping Christians and local churches grow. We believe that God's growth process always starts with hearing clearly what he has said to us through his timeless word—the Bible.

Ever since we opened our doors in 1991, we have been striving to produce resources that honour God in the way the Bible is used. We have grown to become an international provider of user-friendly resources to the Christian community, with believers of all backgrounds and denominations using our Bible studies, books, evangelistic resources, DVD-based courses and training events.

We want to equip ordinary Christians to live for Christ day by day, and churches to grow in their knowledge of God, their love for one another, and the effectiveness of their outreach.

Call us for a discussion of your needs or visit one of our local websites for more information on the resources and services we provide.

UK & Europe: www.thegoodbook.co.uk
North America: www.thegoodbook.com
Australia: www.thegoodbook.com.au
New Zealand: www.thegoodbook.co.nz

UK & Europe: 0333 123 0880
North America: 866 244 2165
Australia: (02) 6100 4211
New Zealand (+64) 3 343 1990

www.christianityexplored.org

Our partner site is a great place for those exploring the Christian faith, with a clear explanation of the good news, powerful testimonies and answers to difficult questions.

One life. What's it all about?